This Book Belongs To:

Andrew Joseph Mentel
Birthday Sept. 9, 1989

The Rand McNally Book of
Favorite
All-Time Classics

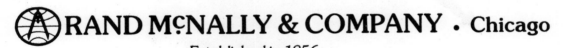

RAND McNALLY & COMPANY • Chicago

Established in 1856

CONTENTS

The Town Mouse and the Country Mouse

A TOWN MOUSE once visited a friend who lived in the country.

For lunch the Country Mouse
served wheat stalks, roots, and
acorns. The Town Mouse ate very
sparingly, nibbling a little of this

and a little of that. She made it very plain that she ate the simple food only to be polite.

After the meal the friends had a long talk, or rather the Town Mouse talked about her life in the city while the Country Mouse listened.

They then went to bed in a
cozy nest in the hedgerow and
slept in quiet and comfort.

In her sleep the Country Mouse dreamed she was a Town Mouse with all the luxuries and delights of city life that her friend had described.

So the next day when the Town Mouse asked the Country Mouse to go home with her to the city, she gladly said yes.

When they reached the mansion
in which the Town Mouse lived,
they found the leavings of a very
fine banquet on the dining
room table.

There were jellies, cakes, and delicious cheeses. Indeed, the most tempting foods that a Mouse can imagine. But just as the Country

Mouse was about to nibble a dainty
crumb of cake, she heard a Cat
meow loudly and scratch at the
door.

In great fear the Mice scurried to a hiding place. They lay quite still for a long time, hardly daring to breathe.

At last they went back to the feast. Then the door opened suddenly. The servants came in to clear the table, followed by the House Dog.

The Country Mouse stopped in
the Town Mouse's den only long
enough to pick up her carpetbag
and umbrella.

"You may have luxuries and dainties that I don't have," she said as she hurried away. "But I

prefer my plain food and simple life
in the country with the peace and
security that go with it."

The Little Red Hen

THERE ONCE lived, in a big barnyard, a Little Red Hen and her brood of little fluffy chicks. She had for neighbors a fat little Pig and a Duck and a Goose.

One day the Little Red Hen found a few grains of wheat scattered about on the ground.

"Cluck! cluck!" called the Little Red Hen, and all her little chicks came running.

The Duck and the Goose came

running, too, thinking the Little
Red Hen had found something
to eat, but the Pig, being so fat
and lazy, just waddled up slowly.

"Cluck! cluck!" said the Little Red Hen. "Just look at these grains of wheat I have found! Now who will help me plant them?"

"Not I," quacked the Duck.

"Nor I," honked the Goose.

"Nor I," grunted the fat little Pig.

"I will plant the wheat myself, then," said the Little Red Hen, and she set to work.

The rain fell and the sun shone, and by and by all the little grains

of wheat sprouted and pushed their bright green blades up through their blanket of earth.

The Little Red Hen had been keeping close watch upon them

as they grew, and when she saw
them all dressed in their golden
holiday clothes she was very
much pleased, indeed.

"The wheat is ripe!" she sang as

she ran about the barnyard.
"Now who will help me cut it?"
"Not I," quacked the Duck.
"Nor I," honked the Goose.
"Nor I," grunted the fat little
Pig from his bed in the shade.

"Then I will cut it myself," declared the Little Red Hen, and she hurried into the barn for a sickle.

She worked long and hard that day, cutting the golden wheat.

"Who will help me thresh the wheat?" she called out one morning bright and early.

"Not I," quacked the Duck.

"Nor I," honked the Goose.

"Nor I," grunted the fat Pig.

"Dear me, then I guess I shall have to thresh it myself," said the Little Red Hen, and into the barn she ran to find a flail. With the flail she beat all the golden grains from the ears.

"Now," said she, bright and early the next morning, "the wheat has been planted and cut and threshed. Who will help me carry it to the mill?"

"Not I," quacked the Duck.

"Nor I," honked the Goose.

"Nor I," grunted the fat Pig.

"Well, in that case," said the Little Red Hen, "I will carry it to the mill myself," and away she ran into the barn to get a sack to carry the wheat in. She filled the sack with the wheat, and threw it over her back. Then away she went toward the mill

to have the wheat ground into flour.

When she had reached the barnyard once more, the Little Red Hen called, "The wheat is

now soft white flour. Who will
help me bake the bread?"
"Not I," quacked the Duck.
"Nor I," honked the Goose.
"Nor I," grunted the fat Pig.

"Then I will bake it myself,"
said the Little Red Hen.
    When at last the bread was
baked, and came out of the oven

in fine big loaves, she set it care-
fully aside to cool and stepped
to the door of her little house.
"Cluck! cluck!" the Little Red

Hen called, and all her little chicks came running.

The Duck and the Goose came running, too. And the fat little Pig also came.

"Now, who will help me eat the
bread?" said the Little Red Hen.
"I will!" quacked the Duck.

"I will, too!" loudly honked the hungry Goose.
"And I!" squealed the fat Pig.

"You remember that I planted the wheat and cut it, I threshed it and carried it to mill, I made the bread and baked it—and now all of you would help me eat it! No, indeed!"

And the Little Red Hen called
all her chicks into the house and
shut the door tight.

"Oh, dear! Oh, dear!" quacked
the Duck. "Why did I not help
the Little Red Hen? Then I should
have had fine white bread, too."

"What a lazy dunce I have been," hissed the Goose to herself.

"Oink! oink!" grunted the fat little Pig sadly. "A little work and a little less sleep wouldn't have hurt me any."

But the Little Red Hen who had worked so hard was happy, and she sang as she cut thick slices of the fresh bread and spread them with butter and jam for her hungry little chicks.

The Three Little Pigs

THERE WAS ONCE a mother pig who had three little pigs. One day they told mother pig they wanted to go seek their fortunes. She gave them her blessing.

So the three little pigs trotted out into the world.

The first little pig had not gone far when he met a man with a cart of straw.

"Please, man, may I have some straw to build a house?" he asked.

The man gave him the straw, and the little pig built a house.

Before long a wolf passed that way, knocked at the door of the little straw house, and called out, "Little pig, little pig, let me come in."

"No, no, by the hair of my chinny, chin, chin," answered the little pig. "Then I'll huff, and I'll puff, and I'll *blow* your house in," said the wolf.

So he huffed, and he puffed, and he blew the house in. But the little pig had slipped away into the woods.

The second little pig met a man with a wagon of sticks.

"Please, man, may I have some sticks to build a house?" he asked.

The man gave him the sticks, and the little pig built a house.

Then along came the wolf, knocked at the door, and called out, "Little pig, little pig, let me come in."

"No, no, by the hair of my chinny, chin, chin," answered the little pig.

"Then I'll huff, and I'll puff, and I'll *blow* your house in," said the wolf.

So he huffed, and he puffed, and he huffed and he puffed, and at last he blew the house in. But the second little pig had slipped out the back door and hidden in the thicket.

The third little pig met a man
with a load of bricks.

"Please, man, do you have some
extra bricks so I can build a house?"
he asked.

The man did, and gave him the
bricks, and the little pig built a house.

Then along came the wolf, knocked at the door, and called out, "Little pig, little pig, let me come in."

"No, no, by the hair of my chinny, chin, chin," answered the little pig.

"Then I'll huff, and I'll puff, and
I'll *blow* your house in," said the wolf.

So he huffed, and he puffed, and
he huffed and he puffed, and he huffed
and he puffed, and still he could not
blow the house in.

At last, when the wolf found out he could not blow the little house in, he called out, "Little pig, little pig, I know where there is a nice apple tree."

"Oh, do you? Where?" asked the little pig.

"Down at Merry-Orchard. Would you like to come with me to get some apples at six o'clock tomorrow morning?"

"Yes," said the little pig.

The next morning the little pig got up at five o'clock and went to the orchard. He climbed an apple tree and was eating a ripe, rosy-cheeked apple when, lo and behold! there was Mr. Wolf below.

"Ah, ha! little pig, so you are here before me," said the wolf. "Is the apple good?"

"Yes, very," said the little pig, trembling. "I will throw you one. Here you are," and he threw an apple toward a hillslope.

Then it rolled and rolled, and the wolf had to run after it. While the wolf was racing to pick up the apple, the little pig climbed down quickly, and ran till he reached home safe and sound.

The next morning the wolf came again to the little pig's house and called out, "Little pig, little pig, I know where there is a fair."

"Oh, do you? Where?" asked the little pig.

"At Shanklin. Would you like to go with me at three o'clock this afternoon?"

"Yes," said the little pig.

So the little pig went to the fair at two o'clock and bought a butter churn. On his way home he saw the wolf coming up the hill! He was frightened and did not know what to do. So he jumped into the butter churn to hide.

It tipped over and rolled down the hill with the pig inside. This gave the wolf such a fright that he did not go to the fair, but trotted slowly home.

The following day he went round to the little pig's house, and called out, "Little pig, little pig, I got a fright, I can tell you, as I went to the fair yesterday. A big round thing rolled down the hill and nearly knocked me over."

"Ho, ho, ho, ho!" laughed the little pig. "Afraid, were you? Well, I can tell you about that. The big round thing was a butter churn that I bought at the fair, and I was inside it."

Then the wolf was angrier than ever and called out, "Now, little pig, I mean to eat you up, anyhow. I'm coming down the chimney."

"Oh, are you?" said the little pig, and as the wolf jumped down, the little pig took the lid off a large pot of boiling water that was on the fire. The wolf tumbled into the bubbling pot. Then the little pig popped on the cover again.

So there was the end of the wolf, and the little pig lived happily ever afterward.

Mary Had a Little Lamb

Mary had
a little lamb,
Its fleece
was white
as snow,

And everywhere

that Mary

went

The lamb

was sure

to go.

He followed her
to school one day,

Which was against the rule.

It made the

children laugh

and play

To see a lamb

at school.

And so

the teacher

turned him out,

But still

he lingered near,

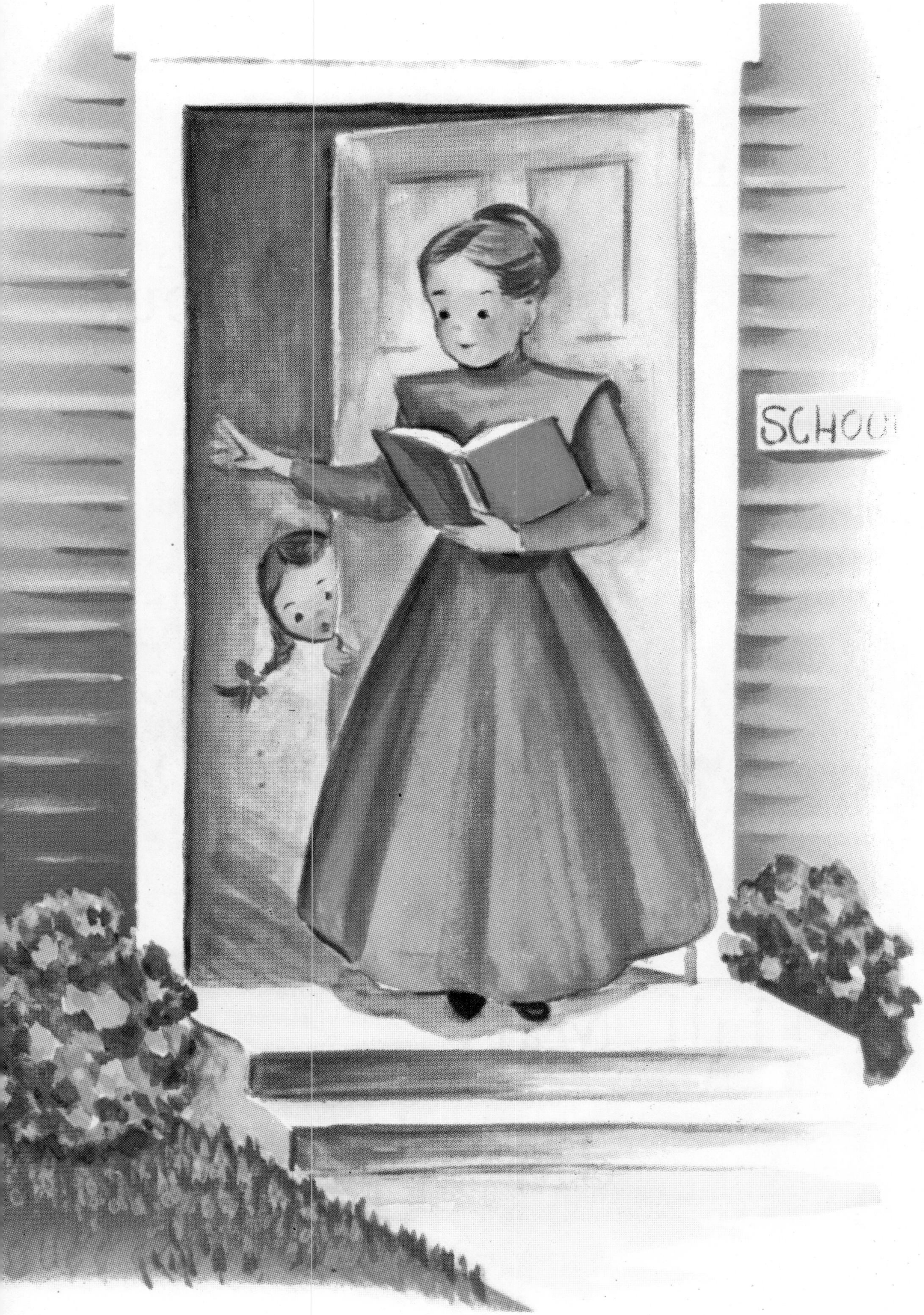
SCHOO

And waited

    patiently about

Till Mary

    did appear.

Then he ran

to her

and laid

His head

upon

her arm,

As if he said,
"I'm not
afraid—
You'll keep me
from
all harm."

"What makes
the lamb love
Mary so?"
The eager
children cry.

"Oh, Mary loves
the lamb,
you know,"
The teacher
did reply.

And you
each gentle
animal
In confidence
may bind,

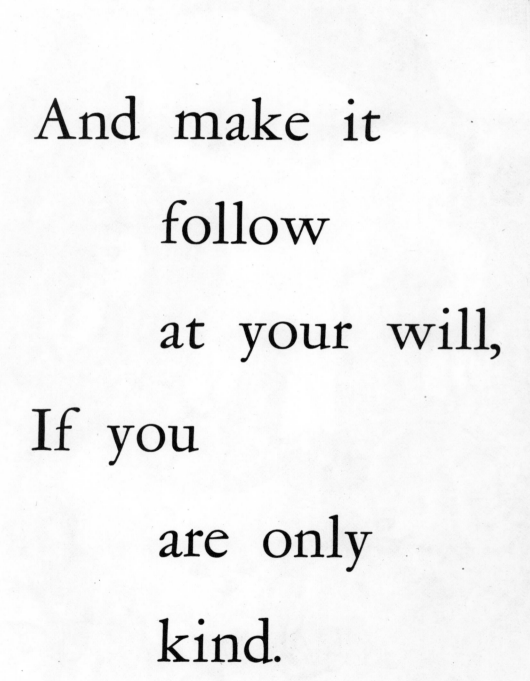

And make it
follow
at your will,
If you
are only
kind.